D0452999

for

CELIA and DOUGLAS

ORCHARD BOOKS
96 Leonard Street, London EC2A 4RH
Orchard Books Australia
14 Mars Road, Lane Cover, NSW 2066
ISBN 1 86039 968 4 (hardback)
ISBN 1 86039 090 0 (paperback)
First published in Great Britain in 1996
First paperback publication 1996

A CIP catalogue record for this book is available from the British Library.
Printed in Belgium

Charlie's Choice

Nicola Smee

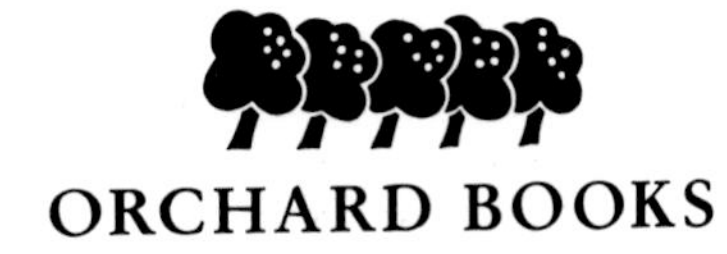

ORCHARD BOOKS

One Saturday morning
Grandpa invited Charlie
to stay for the night.

"Thanks Grandpa,
I'd like that,"
said Charlie.

Charlie ran upstairs to pack.
"You don't need to take all that!"
said Mum, "and just take ONE of your toys."

The toys all wondered which
one of them he'd take.
But not for long...

Mr Monkey had decided.
"Charlie's sure to pick me.
After all, I am the one who
takes him on adventures, and
this will certainly be an adventure!"

"But I'm his Big Blue Bear
and we growl at each other
and feed each other
spoonfuls of honey.

Charlie can't do without me,
not even for one day – he told me so!"
said Big Blue Bear.

Grrrrrrrr!

"I'm afraid you're both going to be disappointed then," said Tiger Puppet.

"Charlie's bound to take me.
We're very good at entertaining people
and Grandpa likes a good laugh,
I've heard him!"

"There's no way I'll be left behind!"
said Percy Penguin.

"I join Charlie in the bath every
night and make sure he's clean.
His mum says I do a good job!"

The toys started squabbling.
Each thought they would be needed more than the other, so it was some time before they noticed Little Mouse squeaking in the background,
"What about me?
What about me!"

“You!” laughed all the other toys.
“Why on earth should Charlie
choose you, Little Mouse?
Your job is the least important,
if you can even call it a job!”

Charlie looked
at his toys
and thought
long and hard.

He loved them all
and he loved visiting Grandpa
but this time he was staying
ALL NIGHT in the SPARE ROOM!

"Get a move on Charlie,"
Mum shouted up the stairs,
"Grandpa's here!"

Charlie
had decided...

Little Mouse's job of
sleeping on Charlie's pillow
was important after all!

If you like Charlie's Choice try reading...

ISBN 1 85213 848 3 (pb) ISBN 1 85213 542 5 (hb)

"A lovely book to share with the under-sixes which can be interpreted on a number of levels."

SCHOOL LIBRARIAN

"Wonderful watercolours combine with simple text to capture Lizzie's anxiety and distress, then her joy of being reunited with a favourite toy."

PRACTICAL PARENTING